Henri Matisse
COLORING BOOK

Far northern France is a gray, rainy place. Nothing could be more different from the paintings made by Henri Matisse, full of sunshine, joy, and bursts of color. Still, that gray land is where Matisse was born and grew up— how is that possible? Maybe the people who suffer the worst weather most appreciate and celebrate the best weather. Certainly they deserve big bouquets of the first blooms of spring.

Matisse often painted flowers, and he also loved open windows, bright cloth, women dressed exotically. He did not follow the old rules about shading or careful proportions, choosing instead to make pictures by combining big areas of color. Those blues and reds and greens are shown inside the cover of this book, but you are invited to invent your own combinations when you color in the following pages.

The eighteen works in this coloring book are from the collection of the Barnes Foundation in Pennsylvania, established by Dr. Albert C. Barnes in 1922 to "promote the advancement of education and the appreciation of the fine arts."

THE BARNES FOUNDATION

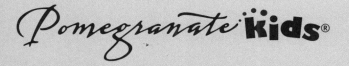

All works of art are from the collection of the Barnes Foundation.

1. *Young Girl on a Balcony over the Ocean (Jeune fille au balcon sur la mer)*, April 1918. Oil on canvas (later mounted to fiberboard), 16 x 12⅞ in. (40.7 x 32.7 cm). The Barnes Foundation BF882.

2. *The Green Dress (La Robe verte)*, between January and June 1919. Oil on canvas (later mounted to fiberboard), 16¼ x 13³⁄₁₆ in. (41.3 x 33.5 cm). The Barnes Foundation BF891.

3. *Domino Players (Les Joueuses de dominos)*, between September 1920 and May 1921. Oil on canvas, 23¹³⁄₁₆ x 28¹³⁄₁₆ in. (60.5 x 73.2 cm). The Barnes Foundation BF889.

4. *Red Madras Headdress (Le Madras rouge)*, between the end of April and mid-July 1907. Oil on canvas, 39⅜ x 31⅞ in. (100 x 81 cm). The Barnes Foundation BF448.

5. *Still Life with Gourds (Nature morte aux coloquintes)*, July 1916. Oil on canvas, 39⅜ x 32 in. (100 x 81.3 cm). The Barnes Foundation BF313.

6. *Woman and Screen (La Femme au paravent)*, between June and September 1919. Oil on canvas (later mounted to cardboard and fiberboard), 13⅜ x 16⅝ in. (34 x 42.2 cm). The Barnes Foundation BF879.

7. *Head of a Young Girl (Tête de fillette)*, 1917. Oil on wood panel, 13¾ x 10½ in. (34.9 x 26.7 cm). The Barnes Foundation BF905.

8. *Chinese Casket (Le Coffret chinois)*, between August and early fall 1922. Oil on canvas, 23¾ x 29⅛ in. (60.4 x 74 cm). The Barnes Foundation BF916.

9. *Woman Reclining*, between April and May 1921. Oil on canvas, 21½ x 25¾ in. (54.6 x 65.4 cm). The Barnes Foundation BF195.

10. *Three Sisters with an African Sculpture (Les Trois soeurs à la sculpture africaine)*, between May and mid-July 1917. Oil on canvas, 77⅛ x 38¼ in. (195.9 x 97.2 cm). The Barnes Foundation BF363.

11. *Three Sisters with Grey Background (Les Trois soeurs sur fond gris)*, between May and mid-July 1917. Oil on canvas, 77 x 38 in. (195.6 x 96.5 cm). The Barnes Foundation BF888.

12. *Three Sisters and "The Rose Marble Table" (Les Trois soeurs à "La Table de marbre rose")*, between April and May 1917. Oil on canvas, 76½ x 37⅞ in. (194.3 x 96.2 cm). The Barnes Foundation BF25.

13. *Two Young Girls in a Red and Yellow Interior (Deux fillettes, fond jaune et rouge)*, between May and June 1947. Oil on canvas, 24 x 19⅝ in. (61 x 49.8 cm). The Barnes Foundation BF2075.

14. *The Red Sofa (Le Canapé rouge)*, between September 1920 and May 1921. Oil on canvas, 10¾ x 18¼ in. (27.3 x 46.4 cm). The Barnes Foundation BF898.

15. *Woman on a Red Sofa (Femme sur un canapé rouge)*, between December 1919 and May 1920. Oil on canvas, 13 x 21⅝ in. (33 x 55 cm). The Barnes Foundation BF914.

16. *The Music Lesson*, summer 1917. Oil on canvas, 96½ x 83 in. (245.1 x 210.8 cm). The Barnes Foundation BF717.

17. *Seated Riffian (Le Rifain assis)*, between November and December 1912. Oil on canvas, 78⅞ x 63¼ in. (200.3 x 160.7 cm). The Barnes Foundation BF264.

18. *Figure with Bouquet*, August 1939. Oil on canvas, 36¼ x 29 in. (92.1 x 73.7 cm). The Barnes Foundation BF980.

•••

Pomegranate Communications, Inc.
Box 808022, Petaluma CA 94975
800 227 1428   www.pomegranate.com

© 2012 The Barnes Foundation™
Artworks by Matisse © Succession H. Matisse /
Artists Rights Society (ARS), New York

www.barnesfoundation.org

Catalog No. CB141

Designed and rendered by Susan Koop

Printed in Korea

21 20 19 18 17 16 15 14 13 12   10 9 8 7 6 5 4 3 2 1

Pomegranate Europe Ltd.
Unit 1, Heathcote Business Centre, Hurlbutt Road
Warwick, Warwickshire CV34 6TD, UK
[+44] 0 1926 430111
sales@pomeurope.co.uk

This product is in compliance with the Consumer Product Safety Improvement Act of 2008 (CPSIA).
A General Conformity Certificate concerning Pomegranate's compliance with the CPSIA is available on our website at www.pomegranate.com, or by request at 800 227 1428.
For additional CPSIA-required tracking details, contact Pomegranate at 800 227 1428.

1. *Young Girl on a Balcony over the Ocean*

2. The Green Dress

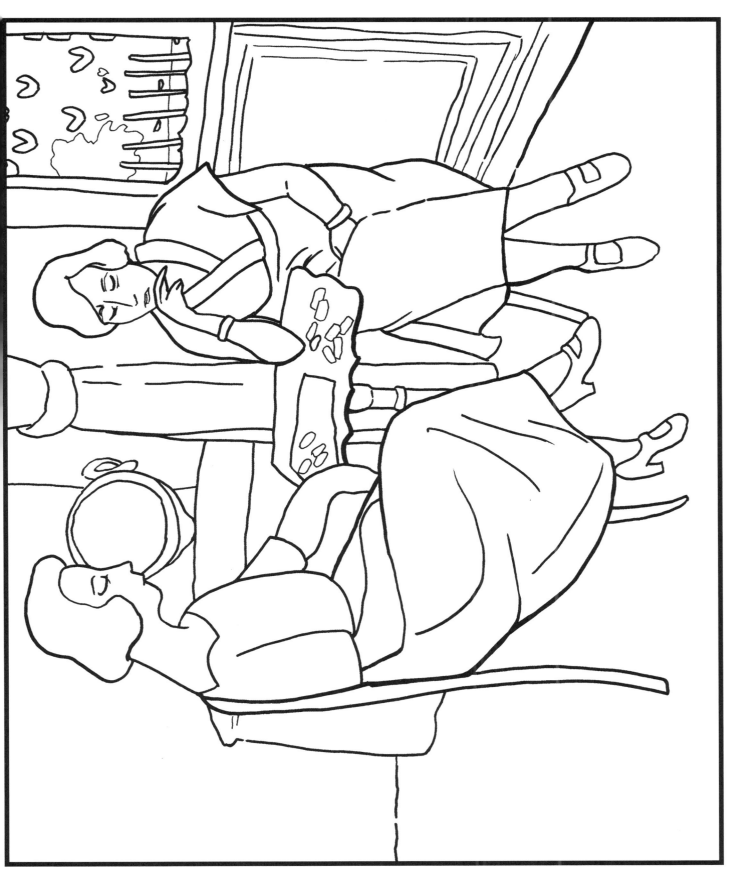

3. Domino Players

4. Red Madras Headdress

5. *Still Life with Gourds*

6. *Woman and Screen*

7. Head of a Young Girl

8. Chinese Casket

9. Woman Reclining

10. *Three Sisters with an African Sculpture*

11. *Three Sisters with Grey Background*

12. *Three Sisters and "The Rose Marble Table"*

13. Two Young Girls in a Red and Yellow Interior

15. *Woman on a Red Sofa*

16. *The Music Lesson*

17. Seated Riffian

18. *Figure with Bouquet*

Draw and color your own picture here!

Draw and color your own picture here!

Draw and color your own picture here!

Draw and color your own picture here!

Draw and color your own picture here!